*This book
belongs to...*

The
Forest Fairies

Illustrated by

Margaret W. Tarrant

Original poetry by

Marion St. John Webb

Series Editor
Fiona Waters

·MARGARET TARRANT'S·
FAIRIES & FLOWERS

First published in this format in 2002 by
The Medici Society Ltd
Grafton House, Hyde Estate Road, London NW9 6JZ

Copyright © The Medici Society Ltd 2002 / 1925

First published in 1925 by The Medici Society Ltd
3 5 7 9 10 8 6 4 2

A catalogue record for this book is available from the British Library.

ISBN 0 85503 254 5

Margaret Tarrant's original artworks have been rescanned for this re-designed edition.

Designed by Tony Potter Publishing Ltd

Printed in Singapore

The
Forest Fairies

Contents

Half a Fairy   ...   7

The Stolen Patch ...   13

Paint Pots ...   17

The Fairy Ring ...   23

The Spider and the Elf-cup ...   29

A Letter to a Noisy Goblin   ...   35

Margaret Winifred Tarrant ...   40

Half a Fairy

It's better to be a bit of a fairy,
Than not be a fairy at all.
I know someone, half a fairy,
Who lives by a forest tall.
She looks like everyone else by day,
As she sweeps up the leaves and sings.
But at night she takes from her kitchen shelf
A pair of fairy wings!
And one of the wings I pin on to her,
And the other she pins on me.
We lock up the house, and both set out;
And, as we look back, we can see
The firelight gleam through the
    window pane,
A tiny flickery light.
We laugh, and then hand in hand we run
Into the moonlit night.

We're each of us only half a fairy,
Sharing a pair of wings.
But out in the forest on moonlit nights,
We see some wonderful things:
Fairies dancing in the windflowers,
And teasing an old brown owl:
While down the path, around the toadstools,
Fat little goblins prowl.

Witches boiling a pot of spells,
Making their dreams come true.
As we both hide, we watch and listen,
And learn the magic too.
For wherever we fly, and wherever we sing,
As we dance through the trees so tall,
It's better to be a bit of a fairy,
Than not be a fairy at all!

The Stolen Patch

A crying little fairy found
A patch of moonlight on the ground.
She knew it was the very thing
To mend the hole torn in her wing.

She dried her eyes, and picked up the patch,
Then sewed it on, what a perfect match!

She flew swiftly away so did not see
Her secret kept by the old larch tree.
It waved its branches round and round,
Mixing the patches all on the ground.

So that the moon would never guess
She had one patch of moonlight less!

Paint Pots

Four forest fairies
What have they got?
Each one carrying
Some paint in a pot..

"We don't like the forest's dark
colours," they said.
"So let's make it much more cheerful instead.
Bright colours we'll pick
For every stone and stick.
Now spread it on thick!"

They crept through the forest as it grew light.
"Let's paint this fat toadstool, and make it
    look bright.
We'll give it a new hat
As easy as that,"
They said to the toadstool so fat.

But one of them soon let his paintbrush fall,
And said, looking up through the dark
    trees tall,
"I'll paint the pale moon
Before she fades so soon
She'll be gone by noon."

The three others laughed, and they started
  to sing:
"You can't paint the moon, you silly
  young thing!
No, certainly not.
Now here's your pot
Paint what you've got!"

The small fairy sighed, and he shook his
    brown head.
"Then I'll *dream* that I'm painting the
    moon," he said.
So he slept on the ground
While the others painted round
The fat little toadstool they'd found.

        Four forest fairies
        What have they got?
        Three quite empty
        And one full pot!

The Fairy Ring

By a clearing in the forest
  We once found a Fairy Ring.
So we hid, to see if fairies
Really came to dance and sing,
In that circle on the ground.
Would they dance and dance around?

Long we waited, still and quiet,
Then something moved, or so it seemed;
Something rustled by the toadstools;
Something fluttered; something gleamed.
Then a rushing in the air!
Could there be someone there?

Then we saw them, tiny fairies,
Moving swiftly up and down,
Dressed in green and blue and silver;
Little goblins, dressed in brown.
And they all began to sing,
Dancing round the Fairy Ring.

Holding hands, in the magic circle,
"Faster, faster!" a fairy cried.
On they danced, and never noticed
One of them was left outside,
Sitting on a mossy stone,
One small goblin, all alone.

"I can't dance," we heard him crying,
"I have lost my dancing shoes.
I've lost my voice, and so no singing.
You are selfish, all of you.
I can't dance and play and so
Why should you, I'd like to know!"

The naughty little goblin sat
And frowned and sulked a while.
He looked so cross and grumpy
That we both began to smile.
We forgot we had to hide,
And we moved a step outside.

Then at once there was a rushing,
And a frightened flurry
As the fairies quickly scattered,
Rushed away all in a hurry,
Little frightened, startled things.
In an instant they all had flown
And we were left there, quite alone.

The Spider and the
Elf-cup

Elf-cup! Elf-cup!
Spinning my web, I have spied you,
Up in the tree,
What else can I see?
Is that a fairy sitting beside you?

Elf-cup! Elf-cup!
Is that a goblin I see peeping
Over your rim?
Yes, I see him
As nearer and nearer I'm creeping.

Elf-cup! Elf-cup!
The stories are so strange,
But is it true
If I drink from you,
Into a fairy I will change?

Elf-cup! Elf-cup!
It is dew-drops you hold, I knew it!
Shall I drink it up,
All the dew from your cup?
Now tell me, how do I do it?

A Letter to a
Noisy Goblin

Dear Sir,

I'm going to put this letter
  Down the hole beside the tree.
I think it is your front door
Or so it seems to be.
Your name I do not know
But I hope you get this letter
As you sit there down below.

I am sorry to complain
But my poor old head does ache.
For every night without fail
Such a dreadful noise you make.
I hear you through my window
As I try to go to sleep.
You start playing with the catkins
And pretend that they are sheep.
And you pretend there is a stile
You want them to jump over,
And you're calling, all the while,
"Over the stile!
Over the stile!"

And since the catkins cannot move,
For they're growing on a tree,
You climb up high then pull them hard
And watch them tumble free.
And when at last you shake them off,
They fall down to the ground.
Then you begin to shriek and laugh,
And dance around and round.
And you're calling all the while
"Over the stile!
Over the stile!"

It makes me turn and toss about
And keeps me wide awake.
I wish you'd play a quieter game.
Please do, for goodness sake!
I'm tired of hearing all the while,
"Over the stile!
Over the stile!"

So I'm going out this evening
To the hole beside the tree,
And if it is your front door
You'll get this note from me.

Margaret Winifred Tarrant (1888 - 1959)

'Every time a child says, " I don't believe in fairies," ' warned Peter Pan, 'there is a little fairy somewhere that falls down dead.' By her paintings Margaret Tarrant did as much to encourage children's belief in fairies as J M Barrie did by his writings. Born in London in 1888, the only child of artist Percy Tarrant and his wife Sarah, Margaret excelled at art from an early age, and she was only 19 when she received her first, very prestigious, commission, from J M Dent & Sons: to illustrate Charles Kingsley's much-loved children's classic, *The Water Babies*, which was first published in 1863.

Her delicate, charming pictures matched the spirit of the story perfectly and earned her a string of new commissions: *Nursery Rhymes* (1914 and 1923), *Alice in Wonderland* (1916) and

Hans Andersen's Fairy Tales (1917) for Ward Lock & Co., plus postcards for Oxford University Press.

Margaret Tarrant illustrated some 20 books for George G. Harrap & Co. between 1915 and 1929, but an even more important publishing relationship began in 1920, when she completed her first pieces for The Medici Society. This was to prove a long and fruitful connection, resulting in most of her best-known work. In the 1920s, for example, she illustrated this highly successful series of fairy books for the company, written by the poet and author Marion St John Webb. Her picture of Peter's Friends, inspired by J M Barrie's *Peter Pan* stories and the statue in Kensington Gardens, proved so popular when it appeared in 1921 that it had to be reproduced many times.

Peter's Friends

The dusk of the nineteenth and dawn of the twentieth centuries were magical times for fairy lovers. Fascination with fairy lore was widespread, reaching unprecedented heights in 1922 when Sir Arthur Conan Doyle published *The Coming of the Fairies*, containing 'photographs' of fairies taken by two young girls in a Yorkshire village, which were later proved to be hoaxes. The story was actually a fascinating deception, which was believed by many reputable people. The mystery was not solved until towards the end of the twentieth century, when the girls involved, now elderly ladies, explained what had really happened.

In 1922, Margaret Tarrant's *Do You Believe in Fairies?* showed two children encircled by a ring of fairies, which caught the public excitement already created by Sir Arthur Conan Doyle's book.

Do You Believe in Fairies?

This interest was mirrored in an outpouring of art and literature. Children's books cultivated belief in fairies: they were used in religious teaching, magazines were devoted to them, and captivating new works appeared, most notably J M Barrie's *Peter Pan* and *Peter Pan in Kensington Gardens*. Rudyard Kipling wrote *Rewards and Fairies* and even Beatrix Potter embraced the subject in *The Fairy Caravan*.

Artists revelled in the opportunity to portray imaginary worlds. Arthur Rackham, the most fashionable illustrator of his day, depicted a sinister fantasy landscape, peopled by spiky goblins, fairies and mice amid gnarled trees with gnomelike faces. In contrast, Honor Appleton, Maud Tindal Atkinson and Mabel Lucie Atwell offered gentler, comforting images recalling Kate Greenaway's illustrations of apple-cheeked children.

Margaret Tarrant was one of those most associated with the depiction of fairies in the 1920s and 1930s, together with her friend and sketching partner, Cicely Mary Barker (1895 - 1973). Both began to use Art Nouveau and Arts and Crafts

elements in their work, and in Tarrant's
paintings a breathtaking attention to detail -
diaphanous wings with the intricate tracery of a
dragonfly's wings - is a testament to the reality
of fairies, imaginary or otherwise.

During her life Margaret Tarrant tackled a wide
range of subjects and won special acclaim for
those, such as *All Things Wise and Wonderful*,
with a religious theme. But her forte was fairies,
for in her evocation of these ethereal figures she
could express her love for children, wild flowers
and dance, of all that was beautiful and pure.

She would sketch meticulously
from life to capture the
likeness of a child or plant,
then compose her pictures by
arranging the subjects in
imaginary settings, infusing
them with a distinctive
otherworldly quality.

Margaret Tarrant's fairies have a unique fluidity and balletic grace that expressed her delight in the free-flowing dance invented by Isadora Duncan. She was very much a free spirit herself, flying along the country lanes around her home in Surrey on an ancient bicycle, leaping off impulsively to sketch a flower or help a toddler to paint. She never married, but she attracted many friends by her generosity, energy and zest for life. Perhaps it was this childlike enthusiasm and innocence, combined with a special kind of imagination, that gave her a natural affinity with fairies.

The Lily Pool

Much missed when she died in 1959, Margaret Tarrant left a lasting legacy in charming pictures that seem as fresh today as the day they were painted, and still enchant new generations with their glimpses into a secret fairy world.

The new edition

There are 12 beautiful fairy books by Margaret Tarrant, originally published between 1923 - 1928. The re-designed edition is now available to collect as a set, with modern scanning methods used to bring out the exquisite detail of the original paintings and drawings.